Invitation to Madrigals 2

A graded selection of 20 four-part works
transcribed and edited by
THURSTON DART
for SATB

Stainer & Bell

© 1962 Stainer & Bell Ltd
23 Gruneisen Road, London N3 1DZ

Reprinted 1978, 1987, 1990 and 1996

ISBN 0 85249 309 6

Printed in Great Britain by Galliard (Printers) Ltd, Great Yarmouth

CONTENTS

				page
	Foreword			iv
1.	Deo gratias	*William Byrd*	1605	6
2.	Since first I saw your face	*Thomas Ford*	1607	8
3.	April is in my mistress' face	*Thomas Morley*	1594	10
4.	Since my tears and lamenting	*Thomas Morley*	1594	13
5.	Never weather-beaten sail	*Thomas Campian*	*c.*1613	16
6.	I have ere this time	*Thomas Whythorne*	1571	18
7.	Say, gentle nymphs	*Thomas Morley*	1594	20
8.	Wilt thou, unkind	*John Dowland*	1597	24
9.	In going to my naked bed	*Richard Edwards*	*c.*1560	26
10.	Amyntas with his Phyllis fair	*Francis Pilkington*	**1613**	29
11.	Weep O mine eyes	*John Bennet*	1599	34
12.	Now every tree	*Thomas Weelkes*	1597	36
13.	Lock up, fair lids	*Martin Peerson*	1620	40
14.	Fair Phyllis I saw	*John Farmer*	1599	42
15.	Farewell, dear love	*Robert Jones*	1600	46
16.	Wounded I am	*William Byrd*	1589	48
17.	Phyllis, farewell	*Thomas Bateson*	1604	51
18.	Adieu sweet Amarillis	*John Wilbye*	1598	54
19.	Dear love, be not unkind	*Richard Dering*	1620	58
20.	Pearce did dance	*Giles Farnaby*	1598	60

———————o———————

iv

FOREWORD

THE MADRIGAL was an invention of 14th-century Italy. Laid aside during the whole of the 15th century, it was taken up again in a new form about 1530 and it remained in favour for another hundred years. No-one knows when English musicians first began to sing Italian madrigals, but by 1588 their vogue had become sufficiently great for Nicholas Yonge, a choirman of St. Paul's Cathedral, to issue his famous *Musica Transalpina*. This was a selection of madrigals for four, five and six voices, composed by the leading Italian musicians of the time, together with two stanzas from Ariosto set by William Byrd (1543-1623). Ariosto's poems, like all the others in the collection, were translated into English for Yonge's publication—" brought to speak English ", as the title-page puts it.

Despite Byrd's essays in the new Italian style, the ordinary musical language used by most English composers of his generation was not in the least Italian, as we can tell from such books as Byrd's own *Psalmes, Sonets & Songs* (1588), issued a few months before Yonge's collection, his *Songs of Sundrie Natures* (1589), or Mundy's *Songs and Psalmes* (1594). The poems found in these collections are ungainly and harsh to the ear, the metres jog-trot, the counterpoint rugged, and the harmony restless. Slowly at first and then more compellingly, the elegance and balance of the Italian style took hold of the English imagination in poetry as in music, and moralizing rhymes gave way to sugared sonnets. The publication of Watson's *Italian Madrigalls Englished* (1590) gave momentum to the new trend in music, but the composers of this collection were Italians to a man. The true English madrigal was created almost single-handed by Thomas Morley (*c.* 1558-1602?), chiefly through a sequence of music-books published between 1593 and 1597 containing madrigals, canzonets, balletts, and fantasies of his own composition. The sequence was rounded off with a collection of 4-part canzonets by Italian composers, and a masterly treatise including rules for composing in the newer Italian style—Morley's famous *A Plaine and Easie Introduction to Practicall Musicke* (1597). The music in these books ranged from two-part to seven-part writing (the limits maintained by nearly all the English madrigalists), and the books were an instant success. In the short space of four years Morley had successfully grafted on to an English stock almost every shoot of the Italian madrigal: the madrigal proper, the canzonet, the ballett, the pastoral, the wordless fantasia. Classical in their simplicity, smooth-running in their words, fresh in harmony and counterpoint, Morley's madrigalian writings were models for a whole generation of his friends, colleagues and pupils. The astonishing flowering of the English madrigal during the next thirty years was very largely due to the skill, taste, enterprise and discernment of this one remarkable musician.

The life's work of another remarkable musician, the late Dr. Edmund H. Fellowes, has made the riches of this school of English composers known to countless thousands of music-lovers throughout the world. But few madrigals are simple to perform at first sight, and the present book is an attempt to provide what might perhaps be called a plain and easy introduction to practical madrigal-singing, for soprano, alto, tenor and bass. The madrigals and other works it contains have been newly transcribed and edited from the original sources, and they have been arranged in increasing order of difficulty. For each piece I have added a few notes on rehearsal and performance. The collection illustrates the four seasons of the English madrigal's growth and decay: the stern

Elizabethan winter of Edwards, Whythorne and Byrd; the scented spring of Morley, Wilbye and Farmer; the long Jacobean summer of Ford, Pilkington and Campian; the rich autumn of Dering and Peerson. All of the pieces in the collection were originally composed as quartets, though I have had to make a few transpositions and slight adaptations of the musical texture, to keep within the normal ranges of present-day amateur voices. I have done my best to keep these changes as few as possible, and I have also tried to make them conform to Elizabethan and Jacobean custom.

Numbers 1, 2, 5 and 15 are not madrigals. I have chosen to begin the collection with Byrd's short motet "Deo gratias" to point the fact that madrigals, like motets, are based on the rules of imitative counterpoint; and I have included songs by Ford, Campian and Jones as a reminder of another imported style, the air, which was based largely on French models. The style of English song before the arrival of the madrigal is represented by numbers 6, 9 and 16; number 13 shows the madrigal becoming the part-song.

Madrigals are epigrammatic poems, set as vocal chamber-music; that is to say, they are sung to perfection when there is no more than one voice to a part. Their revival in our own time has shown what enjoyment they can also bring to groups of singers, and all the pieces in this book can sound well when performed by small choirs. The individual voices, like the four vocal parts, should be well balanced among themselves. Whispering the words to the musical rhythms will help with problems of phrasing, stressing, enunciation and meaning. Stressed notes will usually be those that are a little longer or higher than their neighbours. Bar-lines have been put in for convenience, not necessarily to show stress. The original Elizabethan and Jacobean part-books are unbarred, and they contain no dynamics or tempo marks. Each singer was evidently expected to make up his own mind about interpretation, rather than to accept other people's ready-made opinions. High-pitched notes and phrases must not be allowed to cry down the other parts; low notes and phrases should not be too submerged. The words must always be clear, and the tone-colour and dynamics of the music should match the verbal sense as closely as glove fits hand.

In Armada year, when the true English madrigal was still unborn, Byrd wrote "there is not any music of instruments whatsoever, comparable to that which is made of the voices of men, where the voices are good, and the same well sorted and ordered.

Since singing is so good a thing,
I wish all men would learn to sing."

Byrd's most distinguished pupil, Thomas Morley, made the English madrigal, so he is entitled to have the last word about it. In his treatise of 1597 Morley wrote "The best kind of [light music] is termed Madrigal . . . a kind of music made upon songs and sonnets, such as Petrarch and many poets of our time have excelled in . . . As for the music, it is—next unto the Motet—the most artificial, and to men of understanding most delightful . . . You must possess yourself with an amorous humour . . . so that you must in your music be wavering like the wind, sometimes wanton, sometimes drooping, sometimes grave and staid, otherwhile effeminate . . . and the more variety you show the better shall you please ". These were hints to would-be composers, but they still remain the best of guides for performers of these enchanting works.

King's College,
London, W.C.2   THURSTON DART

1 Deo gratias

WILLIAM BYRD (1605)

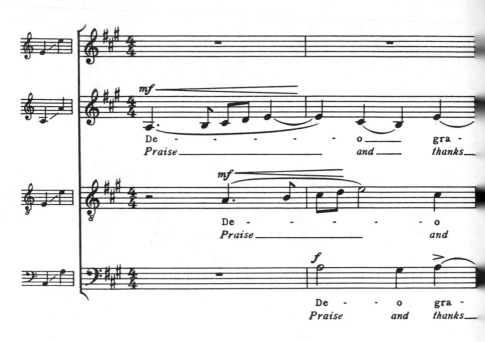

If the style of this motet seems too daunting at first, start with nos. 2 to 7, and then come back to it. Beat a slow 4; let the music flow.

2 Since first I saw your face

THOMAS FORD (1607)

1. Since first I saw your face I re-solv'd to
If now I be dis - dain - ed, I wish my

hon - our and re - nown__ ye; What, I that lov'd and
heart had ne - ver known__ ye.

What, I that lov'd and
heart had ne - ver_ known ye.

hon - our and re - nown ye; What, I that lov'd and
heart had ne - ver_ known ye.

hon - our and re - nown ye; What, I that
heart had ne - ver known ye.__

2. The sun, whose beams most glorious are, rejecteth no beholder,
   And your sweet beauty past compare made my poor eyes the bolder;
   Where beauty moves and wit delights, and signs of kindness bind me,
   There, O there, where e'er I go, I leave my heart behind me.

The top part is the most important (the others accompany), so make it a smooth flowing tune.
The words must be very clear. For a good start, give the third beat.

3 | April is in my mistress' face

THOMAS MORLEY (159

This is a true madrigal—the first ever published by an English composer to English words. 'July' must rhyme with 'truly'. Choose a very moderate tempo. Four seasons in the words: four contrasting moods to be caught in the music.

4 Since my tears and lamenting

THOMAS MORLEY (1594)

Since my tears and lamenting, False love, breed thy content - ing, false love, breed thy content - ing, Still thus to weep for e - ver, still thus to weep for e - ver, These

The words (not the bar-lines) control the stresses. Taut expressive lines at 'Out, alas!'— and the exclamation point must be worked into the phrasing.

5 Never weather-beaten sail

THOMAS CAMPIAN (c. 161?)

1. Ne - ver wea - ther-beat - en sail more
   Ne - ver tir - ed pil - grim's limbs af -

will - ing bent to shore, Than my_ wea - ry_
-fec - ted slum - ber more,

sprite now_ longs to fly_ out_ of my trou - bled breast.
sprite now_ longs to fly out of my trou - bled breast.

2. Ever blooming are the joys of Heav'ns high Paradise:
   Cold age deafs not there our ears, nor vapour dims our eyes;
   Glory there the sun outshines, whose beams the blessed only see.
   O come quickly, O come quickly, O come quickly, glorious Lord, and raise my sprite to Thee

'deafs' = 'deafens'

A sacred song, with long flowing lines. The words matter; so shape and define them. When the
alto rises above the tune, these notes must be very soft.

18

6 I have ere this time

THOMAS WHYTHORNE (157?

Take time while time is, for time will a - way.

I have ere this time heard ma - ny one say:

Take time while time is, for time will a - way,

take time while time is, for time will a - way.

FINE

This is what many English songs were like before they encountered the sun and shadows of Italian madrigals. If you want to know more about Whythorne, read his autobiography. Sing his song with formality, not fast (begin in 6); the sections in 2 or 3 parts may be sung by single voices.

7 Say, gentle nymphs

THOMAS MORLEY (1594

This gentle pastoral requires a gentle tempo and gentle dynamics. Make dotted rhythms neat and unanimous, and the pattern ♩ ♪♪♪ ♪ ♩ very nimble. Beautiful tone pleases.

8 Wilt thou, unkind

JOHN DOWLAND (1597)

well, fare - well. But yet or ere I part (O cru -

fare - well. But yet or ere I part (O cru -

fare - well. But yet or ere I part (O cru -

fare - well. But yet or ere I part (O cru - el),

- el), Kiss me sweet, kiss me sweet, sweet my jew-el. Fare- jew-el.

- el), Kiss me sweet, kiss me sweet, sweet my jew - el. Fare-well, -el.

- el), Kiss me, kiss me sweet my jew - el. Fare-well, -el.

Kiss me sweet, kiss me sweet, kiss me, my jew - el. Fare-well, -el.

2. If no delays can move thee,
   Life shall die, death shall live
     Still to love thee.
   Farewell, *etc*.

3. Yet be thou mindful ever,
   Heat from fire, fire from heat
     None can sever.
   Farewell, *etc*.

Dowland has matched paradox in words with cross-accent in music - to make a game of love.
Point the words: counterpoint the phrases. 'reave' = 'bereave'.

9 In going to my naked bed

RICHARD EDWARDS (c.1560)

In going to my naked bed,
In going to my bed, my naked bed,
In going to bed, as one that would have
In going to my bed, as

as one that would have slept, I heard a wife sing to her
as one that would have slept, I heard a wife sing to her
slept, I heard a wife sing to her
one that would have slept, I heard a wife sing to her child, that

child, that long before had wept. She sigh-ed sore, and sang full sweet to bring
child, that long had wept. She sigh-ed sore, and sang full sweet to bring
child, that long had wept. She sigh-ed sore, and sang full sweet to bring
long before had wept. She sigh-ed sore, and sang full sweet to bring

This is fairly difficult, and you may like to come back to it after no. 14. For later handlings of a similar point, see nos. 14 and 10. Sing tenderly and simply—the song is not so easy as it looks. Concentrate on final consonants, for they must all be heard (d, t, tch, ds, b, v, f, ld, pt).

10 Amyntas with his Phyllis fair

FRANCIS PILKINGTON (1613)

Colour words like 'snowy', 'scorching', 'down', 'heav'n', 'hell'. To the Jacobean, as to us, this was a world of make-believe; a touch of cynicism will do no harm.

II Weep O mine eyes

JOHN BENNET (1599

Slow and expressive

Weep O mine

Weep O mine eyes, weep O mine eyes and

Weep O mine eyes and cease not, weep O mine

Weep O mine eyes and cease not, weep

eyes, weep O mine eyes, weep O mine eyes, and cease

cease not, and cease not, weep O mine eyes and cease

eyes & cease not, weep O mine eyes, weep O mine eyes and cease

O mine eyes, weep O mine eyes, weep and cease

not: A - las these your spring-tides, a -

not: A - las these your springtides, a - las these your

not: A - las these your spring - tides, a -

not, and cease not: A - las these your spring-

A miniature lament, composed with great care for detail; the opening points of imitation salute Dowland's famous Lacrimae Pavan ('Flow my tears'). When bass and tenor cross, let the tenor be heard clearly.

12 Now every tree

THOMAS WEELKES (159?

Now e - v'ry tree renews his summer's green, renews his summer's green, summer's news, now e - v'ry tree re-news his summer's green, his summer's green, now e - v'ry tree re-news his summer's green, now e - v'ry tree re-news his summer's green, Why is your heart in winter's garments, why is your heart in winter's green, re-news his summer's green, Why is your heart in winter's green, Why is your heart, why is your heart in green, Why is your heart in winter's garments clad, in

© 1962 by Stainer & Bell Ltd

A love-song of the seasons, like no. 3. Make the contrasts sharp, changing the tempo to fit the mood; and keep up the tone during suspensions.

13 Lock up, fair lids

MARTIN PEERSON (1620)

1. Lock up, fair lids, the trea-sure of my heart; Pre-serve those beams, this a-ge's only light: To her sweet sense, sweet

1. Lock up, lock up, fair lids, the trea-sure of my heart; Pre-serve, pre-serve those beams, this a-ge's only light: To her sweet sense, sweet

1. Lock up, fair lids, the trea-sure of my heart; Pre-serve, pre-serve those beams, this a-ge's only light: To her sweet sense, sweet sleep, some

1. Lock up, fair lids, the trea-sure of my heart; Pre-serve those beams, this a-ge's only light: To her sweet sense, sweet sleep,

2. And while, O sleep, thou closest up her sight,
   Her light, where love did forge his fairest dart:
   O harbour all her limbs in easeful plight;
   Let no strange dream make her fair body start.

The poem, slightly adapted here, is by Sir Philip Sidney. Peerson originally set the first three lines of each verse for solo voice and viols (hence the dynamics suggested). His part-writing has been polished for this version. Don't let the s's sizzle.

14 Fair Phyllis I saw

JOHN FARMER (1599)

44

45

Chapter 3, if you like, of the story begun in nos. 10 and 17—with a happy ending. All voices should practise all versions of the phrases 'but after her lover,' 'up and down he wander'd'. Let the triplets flow easily; tenors, watch the quavers in the 1st-time bar.

15 Farewell, dear love

ROBERT JONES (1600)

1. Fare-well, dear love, since thou wilt needs be gone;
Mine eyes do show my life is al-most done. Nay! I will
nev-er die So long as I can spy. There be ma-ny moe,

2. Farewell, farewell! since this I find is true;
   I will not spend more time in wooing you,
      But I will seek elsewhere
      If I may find her there.
   Shall I bid her go? What and if I do?
   Shall I bid her go, and spare not?
   O, no no no no no, I dare not!

The opening words of this are quoted in *Twelfth Night*, II, 3-though this proves nothing. The chords in the first 12 bars may be sung to 'la' until they are perfectly in tune (concentrate on the tenor E♮ and the bass leaps). 'moe' = 'more'.

16 Wounded I am

WILLIAM BYRD (1589)

Wound-ed I am, and dare not seek re -

Wound - ed I am, and dare not seek re -

Wound - ed I am, and dare not seek re-

Wound-ed I am, and dare not seek

-lief, wound - ed I am, and dare not seek

-lief, wound - ed I am, and dare not seek

-lief, and dare not seek re - lief,

re - lief, For this new

re - lief, For this new stroke, un-seen but not un-felt,

re - lief, For this new stroke, un - seen,

For this new stroke, for this new stroke, un -

A development of the style represented by no.9, with similar problems in rehearsal and performance. Sing with emotion, and bring out the alliteration — blood: bruise / mourn: melt / wounded: witness: wherewith. The top voice must be more prominent throughout.

17 Phyllis, farewell

THOMAS BATESON (1604)

No. 10 was Chapter 1; this is Chapter 2 — a lover's quarrel, full of passion, pain, grief, death, deceit..... and counterfeit. Carry over (in a single breath) all the phrases you can, to make the rests sound like sighs. Check the intonation of C♭, C♯, F♮, F♯, B♭, B♮.

18 Adieu sweet Amarillis

JOHN WILBYE (1598)

56

Here, in less than 50 bars, are all the best features of the English madrigal: sensitivity to words, contrast, contrapuntal pattern, delicate harmonies. Alto and tenor have interchanged a note or two, for ease in performance. Use a new vocal colour for the last 10 bars, and end with a real *pp*.

19 Dear love, be not unkind

RICHARD DERING (1620)

This canzonet shows the influence of the newer Italian style perfected by Monteverdi. The original words were in Italian ('Ardenti miei sospiri'); I have adapted some from a madrigal in East's collection of 1619. Use an extravagant style, with a wide range of dynamic, tempo, colour, rubato. Repeat the first 8½ bars (and/or the last 8½) if you like.

20 Pearce did dance

GILES FARNABY (1598)

The words and underlay have been amended; Farnaby was neat enough in his keyboard music, but he was often clumsy with voices. Both the 'pretty almains' can be found in *The Mulliner Book* (so can no. 9); look them up if you've a chance. Sing rhythmically, but not too fast.

A page from an Elizabethan part-book, slightly reduced in size. It shows the bass voice of Morley's 'April is in my mistress' face' (see no. 3). Madrigals were published in sets of part-books, one for each voice. A set usually contained 21 madrigals.